The Fox and the Crow
and The Ant
and the Grasshopper

Text adapted by Amelia Marshall

Illustrations by Gabriele Antonini
& Barbara Nascimbeni

W

FRANKLIN WATTS
LONDON•SYDNEY

The FOX and the Crow

Illustrated by Barbara Nascimbeni

One day, Crow found some tasty cheese.

Yum, yum!

Fox saw Crow. He saw her tasty cheese, too.

He licked his lips and
thought of a plan.

Mmm, I'm
hungry.

Crow thought she looked and sounded very beautiful.

Fox waited and smiled.
Crow began to sing.

As she opened her beak,
the cheese fell out ...

... straight into Fox's jaws.

Delicious!

Puzzle

Who says it? Match the characters
with their speech bubbles.

1. Yum, yum!

2. Mmm, I'm hungry.

3. Delicious!

4. My cheese!

5. How beautiful you look.

6. I bet you can sing beautifully, too.

Story Quiz

1. What does Crow find?

2. What trick does Fox use on Crow?

3. Why does Crow open her beak?

4. Which words best describe Fox's behaviour?

5. What does Crow learn?

The Ant
and the
Grasshopper

Illustrated by Gabriele Antonini

It was a warm day. Grasshopper sat in the shade, singing happily.

The ants were busy collecting food.

Phew, it's hot!

Winter came. Ant and his friends kept warm with lots of food.

But Grasshopper was cold and hungry.

Shall we help Grasshopper?

The ants decided to share their food.

Remember to get your own food next time!

Puzzle

Who says it? Match the characters with their speech bubbles.

1. Stop working!

2. Where is all your food?

3. Phew, it's hot!

4. I was too busy singing!

5. Can I have some food?

6. Collect your own food next time!

Story Quiz

1. What does Grasshopper do while it is warm and sunny?

2. When winter arrives, what happens to Grasshopper?

3. Why are the ants annoyed with Grasshopper?

4. Who is kind in the story?

5. Who is foolish?

Answers

The Fox and the Crow

Puzzle (page 10)
Fox: 3, 5, 6.
Crow: 1, 2, 4.

Story Quiz (page 11)
1. Some tasty cheese
2. Flattery
3. Crow wants to show off her singing
4. Clever and cunning
5. Not to listen to flattery

The Ant
and the
Grasshopper

Puzzle (page 20)
Ant: 2, 3, 6.
Grasshopper: 1, 4, 5.

Story Quiz (page 21)
1. He rests in the shade and sings
2. He is cold and hungry
3. Because he did not collect his own food
4. The ants
5. Grasshopper

Franklin Watts

First published in Great Britain in 2016 by
The Watts Publishing Group

Text © Franklin Watts 2016
Illustrations for The Fox and the Crow © Barbara Nascimbeni 2009
Illustrations for The Ant and the Grasshopper © Gabriele Antonini 2009

The rights of Amelia Marshall to be identified as the author and Barbara
Nascimbeni and Gabriele Antonini as the illustrators of this Work have been
asserted in accordance with the Copyright,
Designs and Patents Act, 1988.

Series Editor: Melanie Palmer
Series Designer: Peter Scoulding

A CIP catalogue record for this book is available
from the British Library.

ISBN 978 1 4451 4744 4 (hbk)
ISBN 978 1 4451 4745 1 (pbk)
ISBN 978 1 4451 4746 8 (library ebook)

Printed in China

FSC
www.fsc.org
MIX
Paper from
responsible sources
FSC® C104740

Franklin Watts
An imprint of
Hachette Children's Group
Part of The Watts Publishing Group
Carmelite House
50 Victoria Embankment
London EC4Y 0DZ

An Hachette UK company.
www.hachette.co.uk

www.franklinwatts.co.uk

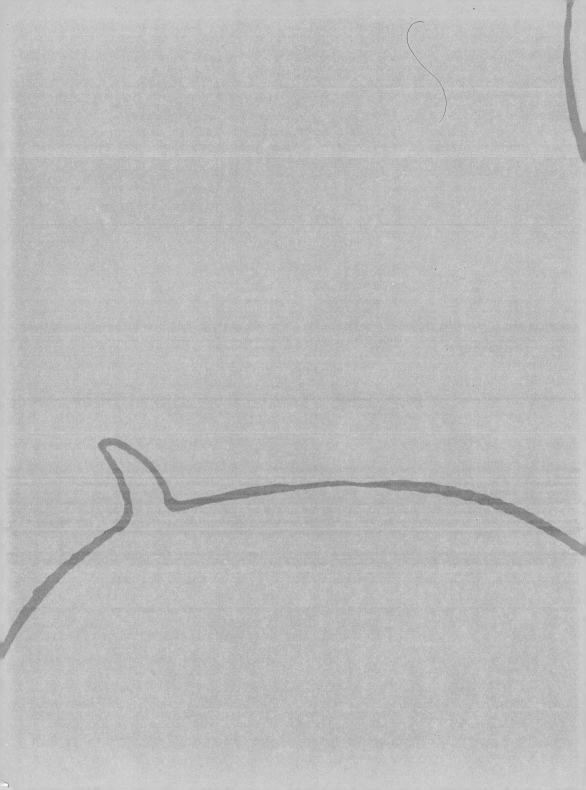